# DATE RAPE by the PASTOR

## A WOLF OUT OF CONTROL

### CEE D. TRUTH

www.rainn.org/statistics

www.yourdictionary.com

Book Cover Design: Prize Publishing House

Printed by: Prize Publishing House, LLC in the United States of America.

First printing edition 2021.

Prize Publishing House

P.O. Box 9856 Chesapeake, VA 23321

www.PrizePublishingHouse.com

Library of Congress Control Number: 2021908949

ISBN (Paperback): 978-1-7371829-2-4

ISBN (E-Book): 978-1-7371829-3-1

# Contents

# Acknowledgments

To all the great pastors who I had the opportunity to be shepherded by. My hat is off to you all. Honorable mentions to the late Bishop S.L. Green of the COGIC, Dr. Jerome Barber of the Sixth Mt. Zion Baptist Temple, and the Elect Bishop Dwight Riddick of Gethsemane Baptist Church.

To all the honest and respectable leaders in the body of Christ who, every day, make it your aim to lead the people of God into all truth and righteousness, I salute you all.

To every man, woman, boy, and girl lifting the blood-stained banner for our Lord and Savior Jesus Christ worldwide, I am sure it is not always easy to live a life of uprightness, especially in this day and time where there seems to be no moral compass and when wrong is considered right and right is looked at as wrong. Keep up the excellent work, don't lose faith because many saints are praying for you all.

To my husband, Joseph, thank you for your support.

To my children, Angelo, Nina, and Rachel thank you all for keeping me grounded.

To my mother, Cynthia, and my brother, Naaman, I am so grateful for the support you have shown me.

To my baby brother, Omar, R.I.P.  I miss you.

To my friend and ex-husband, Willie, you have been there too in your own way.  I thank you.

Please know that I love you all to life.

# If It Had Not Been For the Grace of God

It was January 1st, and the rent was due in four days. I had not heard hide nor hair from my estranged husband. So, of course, I was getting concerned. He was the primary breadwinner for our family. Never mind it was the dead of winter, so it was definitely too cold outside for the girls and me to be facing homelessness.

My husband and I had been married 20 plus years, and for the majority of those years, I was a stay-at-home wife and mother. The man I married had a good heart, although he had now strayed away from home with a co-worker and was now living with her. My source of income was his income, and rightfully so since it was God, the pastor, and I who got him the hookup with one of the largest employers in our city. It was an excellent paying job too, with benefits. That was huge for a black man with just an 11th-grade education. My husband was earning close to $70,000 a year as a blue-collar worker. His trade and skillset were in demand for his industry. It had not always been that way as far as income when we first got married. We were living off the system,

1

food stamps, and rental assistance through the Section 8 government housing program. Yes, he had a job, but it only paid him $5.25 per hour.

We had five mouths to feed, not to mention the clothes we needed to buy for three growing children. Heck, the clothes alone cost just as much as grown folk's clothes which was crazy to me. Being from New York, the fashion capital, we could easily go to the Garment District and buy clothes all day for little to nothing. When I was younger, my two brothers and I could go shopping and get two-piece matching sets, and my mom would only pay one price for the whole set. Here in Virginia, it seemed like the clothing stores were trying to profit quicker by taking the set of clothes, breaking them up, and putting a price tag on each piece.

I quickly turned to the thrift stores for many years when it came to buying my family clothes. That was until the thrift store prices became just as expensive as the big name brand department stores. It was a challenge; however, we made it through those early years with the help of God. I paid tithes, and mixed with faith, I asked God to help give me wisdom and direct my footsteps on how to be like the wise woman in the Bible. He did show me how to manage my husband's income so that it could go further.

If it had not been for the grace of God, I do not know how we would have made it with five people living off of $5.25 an hour and no health benefits other than the free clinic. Well, thank you, God, for the public health clinics. They were truly a Godsend.

*She will do him good and not evil all the days of her life. –*
*Proverbs 31:12, KJV*

# I Know You See Me

Tomorrow was payday, so I had a game plan for getting the rent money from my estranged husband. I was going to head down to his job and meet him at the gate. I lay out my clothes like I was going to a job interview. I had to catch him before he spent the money on his mistress. I set the clock for 4:00 AM. The night went by fast. I showered and got dressed, and told the girls not to open the door. I was going to their dad's job to handle some business.

When I left the house, it was 4:50 AM. It was still dark. I was not used to leaving the apartment that time of the morning. I knew as soon as the car thermostat needle moved just a hair from the red C marks, I was going to hit the gas and boogie out of the apartment complex. Time was of the essence. I had to catch him going into work, or else I might not get another chance since he was now shacking with his love jones in North Carolina. He had met her on the job. From what I understood, she was a co-worker turned lover.

I was not mad nor looking for a fight, just the rent money. I know when relationships start the wrong way most times, they do not last. See God doesn't like ugly even though He made it. *(That's not Scripture, that's just old folk's talk).*

4

When I arrived at the 50th street gate, it was only 5:15 AM. The drive from our house took 10 minutes, and it took me another five minutes to park and walk to the gate. So I would not look too out of place, I stood across the street and scoped out every dark frame that approached the gate in hopes of spotting my estranged husband and getting the rent money or at least a verbal promise to pay. The only thing missing was my "you need Jesus" tracts. I looked like a Jehovah's Witness doing a solo act that morning.

I was pacing up and down the sidewalk, trying to stay warm and trying to see if the next 5'6" slim dark frame was him. The next thing I knew, I saw him, and he saw me, but he slipped into the crowd and hustled into the shipyard gate with the other 20,000 workers. I called his name, but he acted as if he did not hear me nor know me. Wow, how shameful I felt for this man after 20 plus years of marriage and three kids. How could he act like I was a total stranger? I waited and waited, hoping that he would have a change of heart and come back out of the gate to talk to me.

Then the shipyard whistle blew, which meant all the employees were to be in place to start their workday. I felt numb physically from the 30-degree temperature outside, and I was also feeling numb mentally by the cold shoulder my husband had shown towards me. As I stood there in disbelief, I thought to myself, "I have been standing outside in the cold for over two hours waiting to see my estranged husband to get the rent money, and he had the balls to duck me and rush inside the shipyard gate and get lost among the other worker bees." Once the whistle blows, that's the ball game, and I know for sure that meant he would not be coming back out the gate until lunchtime. Wow, was I screwed. There ain't no way I would be back up here to try to catch him by lunchtime. I had to get home to get the girls off to school, then try to figure out what temp agency I was going to sign up with. The ones I heard of pay daily. I would have to work consistently for the next several weeks to get the rent money together. In the meantime, we needed food and money for gas. Well, all hope was not lost. Sister girl always has a Plan A, B, and C. If all else fails, there will be a Plan D too until I work the whole alphabet. I am not giving up, period!!!

*Fret not thyself because of evildoers, neither be thou envious against the workers of iniquity. – Psalm 37:1, KJV*

# Hot Tea, Please

It was now a little after 7:00 AM, and I needed something to warm me up from the cold weather and from the cold shoulder my husband had shown me just a few minutes earlier. I decided to make a pit stop at the little white building that looked like some kind of hole-in-the-wall restaurant. It was just a few feet away from where I had been standing doing my 5:00 AM morning stakeout.

The sun was fully up, but the cold wind was still cutting like a boxcutter. I pull my coat tighter to shield myself from the wind as I started walking towards the little white building. I noticed how dated it looked. Like it had been built in the early '50s or, at best, the early '60s. I could see an air conditioner window unit set in a square shape framed cut-out opening on the front section of the wall. It looked to be about seven feet above the ground. It was the only thing that looked like a window on this little white building. There was also chicken wire around both the window and the AC unit. The closer I got to the front door, I could see that too had issues. The color was not white; it was mud brown. It really looked worn out. I guess from all the years of being handled by the hardworking hands of those shipyard workers, not to mention all the other folks who

7

came in for a quick meal. The door looked like it had been plastered with some kind of cast, the same plaster material you would see on someone with a broken leg cast.

I finally made my way inside the door, which was really heavy, just like those casts from back in the day. I looked around to familiarize myself with the layout since it was my first time in there. All I saw were two Chinese people, a man and a lady, standing behind the counter. The lady asked me if she could help me while the small framed Chinese man with a soiled apron stood in front of a grill flipping a single egg. I assumed he was fixing himself breakfast because there was no one else in the café. The morning shift workers had come and gone, so the next rush would be lunch, so I thought.

Obviously, she was talking to me when she asked again, "Can I help you"?

I replied, "Yes, I want to order a hot cup of tea."

She said okay, and then she turned her back to me for about 30 seconds. While I stared at her back for 10 of those seconds, I took the other 20 seconds to look around the restaurant.

I noticed how really dark and drab it seemed inside. There was only a small amount of sunlight coming inside from the hole in the wall where the portable air conditioner unit sat. I also noticed six old wooden church benches with a picnic table station in front of each bench. The tables did not match the benches. You could tell someone had tried to hand paint the table blue while the benches were a reddish-brown color. I guess all the money they made went into their bank account and not the business, by the look of things. It was definitely a no-frills kind of place to eat or grab something hot to drink.

When I turned back around from checking out the decorum or the lack thereof, I noticed she was looking straight at me. I asked her how much. She said $1.50 while she held the brightest, whitest porcelain teacup I had ever seen. I was impressed. So maybe they were using the money to buy good China. I could see the steam leaping from the hot water that was inside the pretty white teacup. She did not release the cup nor tea bag until I paid her the price she quoted me. I was wondering in my mind, why would a few ounces of hot water and a 10 cent tea bag cost so much?

I was still feeling half frozen, so I went ahead and paid without asking her why she was participating in a price-gouging scheme. I grab the hot cup of tea like a rat grabs cheese. I then looked around for the best seat I could find.

Scanning the room, I spotted a booth tucked away in a far back right corner under an old school heater that hung from the ceiling. I could hear the sound of the blower fan blades turning and cranking out the heat. That was a major clue for me to park myself over there so I could thaw out. I needed to regroup for at least 10 minutes.

While I sipped on my tea, I knew time was of the essence because I would need to get home soon to get the girls off to school. The tea was warming and refreshing. Between the heater overhead and the hot tea, I had to remove my coat because I was starting to perspire. I had one more sip of tea in the cup. The last drop is always the best for me. It is where you get all the good stuff, the residue of the lemon and honey. It's the sweetest part. Heck, for a buck fifty, I wanted it all, every last drop!

*He hath filled the hungry with good things, and the rich he hath sent empty away. – Luke 1:53, KJV*

# I Stayed Too Long

Sometimes we can stay someplace too long. I have heard people say they stayed in a bad relationship too long. I even know you can overstay your welcome at someone's home. To be honest, I realize I overstayed my welcome by sitting in the café too long that day.

It was 7:15 AM, and suddenly the café door flew open. I thought a strong wind had blown it open by how fast and furious the door swung open. However, it wasn't the wind at all. It was several shipyard workers whose shift had just ended, to be exact. I guess they were the salary employees whose shifts end a little later than the hourly workers.

Several men filed into the café, one right after the other. They all went directly to the counter and placed their orders. I sat straight up in my seat because, being somewhat low-key and reserved, I wanted to creep out of there without bringing attention to myself. I tried to ease my coat on, but before I knew it, I saw a man standing at the counter looking my way.

"Uh, Oh," I say to myself. It was a different kind of look. It was *I'm thirsty but not for ice water* kind of look. It seemed as if he was trying to hurry up and place his order with the

11

same lady who took my tea order. He kept looking my way every few seconds. His head turned back and forth like he was watching a tennis match between the US and China. I assumed he was placing an order for some breakfast.

I had no idea some more shipyard workers would be coming in for breakfast. If I had known, I would have been out of here way before then! I would have ordered my tea to go, but I thought I had plenty of time to get my drink on! As far as I knew, the next influx of workers was going to show up from noon for their lunch break until 12:30 PM when their lunch break ended. I just knew for sure I would have the whole spot to myself until I needed to leave to go home around 7:30 AM so I could get the girls off to school by 8:45 AM. What a miscalculation that proved to be.

Speaking of calculation, I could feel his eyes glazing at me, plotting his way over towards me. *Oh boy, here he comes!*

I am not too fond of being interrogated by a total stranger. The first question he asked me was, "What is your name."

I say, "Why, who wants to know."

I guess that was the New York side of me coming out.

He says, "I do."

I ask, "Well, who are you and what is your name." Even though I could clearly see his work badge hanging from his coat with his name and picture, I still inquired. He then confirmed his name, which matched the same information on his work ID. I, in return, told him I was MRS. Anderson. I was hoping that emphasizing the Mrs. part of my title would cause him to turn and leave me alone. Actually, it seemed to have the opposite effect. He started asking me more questions, like what are you doing in here this time of the morning. I told him I came here to meet with my husband before he went off to work. I did not want him to think I was some lady of the night that got caught by daylight and was looking for a John. I mean, Washington Avenue at one point in times past was known for its nightlife, strip clubs, adult shops, and X-rated book stores. Not to mention some of the transgender folks who were very busy doing their thing with the Johns.

I can't judge because we all have a few skeletons in the closet. However, I thank God for His saving power. Plus, here I am dressed to the nine with four-inch heels and a black bodycon dress and trench coat, hair up in a microbraid bun, matching black pocketbook, and accessories sitting in some hole-in-the-wall restaurant 7:30 in the morning would definitely pique some man's curiosity. Maybe that's why the lady who took my tea order looked at me really strange earlier that morning when I first came in the door. I mean, I had to always look my best. The church I attended with my late Bishop did not play that foolishness, nor did his late wife. We, as women, had to look our best because we represented God and His Kingdom. There were no hair bonnets, no pajama pants or slippers when we came out of the house. You better not get caught looking crazy at your child's PTA meeting either. Your feet better not be ashy and crusty. Lord, that was not how we were taught. Our pastor had a reputation for being serious about the issues of life. Some people felt he was too hard on the members, but I needed that teaching. It made me a better wife and mother to my family. So for me to leave to go anywhere without my bath and being fully dressed like a lady was complete no, no! My pastor even taught the men the same principles too.

*For the Lord taketh pleasure in his people: he will beautify the meek with salvation. – Psalm 149:4, KJV.*

# Watch As Well As Pray

Noticing the time, I quickly reached for my coat and pocketbook.

He says, "Wait, are you leaving?"

I say, "Yes," as I had started putting on my coat and buttoning it up.

Here he was, this stranger with a clean-looking appearance, fresh fade haircut, and five o'clock shadow along with a smooth as peanut butter approach, mocha brown skin tone his teeth straight as 32 arrows in a quiver. Not to mention his smile was bright white like 100 snow-capped mountains. I guess he stood 5'11" with a physique like a top senior college draft pick quarterback. His thighs were cut like beef tips on special. It was easy to see the definition of the shape of his legs through his Docker pants legs. His shoulders looked like he had on shoulder pads, but he did not. His arms were popping off a muscle built with pride through his tan members-only jacket. As he spoke to me, his voice seemed to dance with his words which had a rhythm that kept time with the beat of my heart, which was beating fast because of the lateness of the hour and the

15

pressure to get the heck out of this joint and go home to my safe place. It was a bit much, but I played it cool.

He paused for a few seconds as if he was thinking, then he asked me, "Are you walking?"

I say, "No, my car is parked around the corner in the Employees Credit Union lot."

His rebuttal was, "Can I give you a ride to your car?" I say, "No thanks, I can walk."

He seemed to be in some kind of hurry all of a sudden when he saw I was leaving. He says, "Wait, let me get my food, and I will walk out with you."

I hesitated, looking at him while he glared back at me with the biggest blackish color eyeballs, the kind you would see on a dog. He quickly walked to the food counter, paid the lady, and grabbed a greasy bag of food. I was heading towards the front door, but before I could pull on the door handle, he was right on the back of my heels, asking me, "Please, please let me drive you to your car."

I politely refused again. He seemed bent on getting me to accept his offer to get me to my car.

He says, "What's the harm? Besides, it's cold outside, and you are wearing a dress and heels. My vehicle is right over there" while pointing in the direction of the employees' parking lot.

Wow! I thought to myself, this man is really trying to be nice to me. Besides, I have all his information: his name, the first and the last, the address to his job, and even the shipyard's main phone number. I had stored that information on my phone, so if I had to reach out to my husband in an emergency, I could call him with the quickness. Too bad I did not think to call my estranged husband's job a few days earlier when the rent was due or at least left a message with his boss telling him to call home. That may have saved me the trouble of being out there at the shipyard gate at 5:15 AM that Thursday morning. As they say, hindsight is 2020. I told myself, *what the heck? This guy isn't a criminal, or else he would not be working in a white-collar profession. Plus, I am armed with enough information about him that if he tried something crazy, I could lead the police straight to him.*

So I told him, "Okay, you can give me a ride to my car."

*Yea, though I walk through the valley of the shadow of death, I will fear no evil: for thou art with me; thy rod and thy staff they comfort me. – Psalm 23:4, KJV*

17

# Letting My Guard Down

I was standing near the curb waiting for him to reappear from his disappearing act when I noticed a car heading towards me at break-neck speed. You would have thought it was some kind of police vehicle in hot pursuit of someone. No bells or whistles were sounding off, other than the ones in my spirit.

"Be careful," the Holy Spirit spoke, but I thought he was telling me to be careful stepping off the curb in my black four-inch, chunky heel, t-strap, peep toe, suede shoes. They were my favorite pair of shoes at the time because they matched perfectly with my dress. I took my time getting in the car after it stopped rolling on its side, leaning and rolling on its two wheels, looking like a stuntman was driving it. The passenger side door swung open. I could see this stranger's butt was still sitting in the driver's seat as if his behind was stuck there with gorilla glue. He leaned across the gear shift on one arm, and one hand pulled open the door handle from inside his two-seater.

I think he can't really be that much of a gentleman, or else he would have gotten out of his car to open my door. As I made my way inside his car, I knew he should know better

18

than not to get out and open or even close my door. I know he's old enough to know better. I could see some gray hair strands scattered throughout his black, shiny crown, which led me to believe he was a seasoned gentleman even though his physical frame looked like a young, well-built athlete. As soon as I closed my door, I proceeded to give the stranger driving directions to the Employee Credit Union parking lot. Truth be told, he should have already known where it was located since it was only 300 feet away from the café. I gave him directions just the same in case he got confused and headed in a different direction and tried to kidnap me.

It took about 100 seconds for him to drive me to my car. Once the car stopped, I hurried and reached for the door. I told him thanks for the ride.

He said, "You're welcome. Now can I get your phone number?"

Did I have a brain freeze from the cold weather? Was my mind cloudy from the tea? What was I thinking, or was I not thinking? I was new to the game. The game some men play with their prey. I had lived a sheltered life as a wife, mother, and saved church member, which was a good thing. However, at the same time, I was not as watchful nor prayerful as I needed to be at that moment. My main focus was catching up with my estranged husband and getting the

19

rent money before he spent it all on his co-worker turned lover. He and she would be at Applebee's buying drinks and eating off the two for $20 menu until all his money was gone. Worst than that, he and his so-called buddies could lose their shirts at the card table gambling the other half of the night away on payday.

When you are preoccupied with getting your money to meet your basic needs, you can fail to keep a watchful eye open for the adversary.

When he asked me for my phone number I did not think to tell him, *Sir you know I am a married woman and my husband is very jealous and crazy* line, which may have worked! I did not know because I was trying to figure out how to flip the ball back in his court, so I asked him for his phone number.

I said, "How about you give me your phone number instead," hoping he would write it down on a piece of paper that I could throw away ASAP once I got out of his presence.

I guess he saw through that and gave me some bogus excuse about not having his own place or a phone where he could be reached. He said he was staying with a roommate and that he only had a cell phone, pointing to a small flip phone that he pulled out of the upper left-hand side of his jacket pocket. I accepted that fake excuse and gave in to his request to have my phone number. I did not even think to misquote it or even to misprint it so he would not have the correct phone number.

*Be still, and know that I am God: I will be exalted among the heathen, I will be exalted in the earth. – Psalm 46:10, KJV*

# Smooth As Silk

Four days later, my phone rang. I was hoping it was my husband. The caller ID showed the number as private. I thought I better answer because what if it's my husband who God saw fit to have arrested, and he was now calling me from jail to repent for his wicked ways. I quickly pick up the phone and say hello.

"How are you doing?"

I paused for a few seconds because the voice on the other end did not sound like my husband's voice. I was really hoping it was just the same.

I say, "Who is this?"

The man's voice on the other end said, "It's me. Remember, I am the guy who you met in the café last Thursday."

"Oh well, hello me."

He laughed and said, "Oh, you don't remember my name?"

"No."

"That's not fair because I remember your name. It's Candy Anderson, right?"

"Yes, that's right."

"Well, I am Samrick Clark. Remember now?"

"Oh yes, I do now. Good morning Samrick. How have you been doing?"

"Great now that I hear your lovely voice, Candy."

Suddenly the topic changed to what are you doing right now. I told him I was cooking breakfast for me and the girls since they were home from school because of all the snow that had fallen the night before.

"That's really funny," Samrick said as he chuckled. "Guess what? I am being sent home along with all the other shipyard workers because of the snow."

"Oh, okay."

I really did not give too much thought to what he was saying. My main concern at the moment was trying to flip the pancakes before they burn.

Samrick asks, "Well do you think I can stop by for a few minutes before I head home?"

After a brief pause, I say, "I guess."

I thought he really couldn't be that dangerous because he's a white-collar salary worker, and you have to have a background check to work there. Plus, I don't think anyone in their right mind would try something with someone's kids present.

I give him my address, and what seemed like 10 minutes later, I hear a "tap tap" on my front door. I look out the peephole, and it was Samrick. I then open the door, and there he was, flashing a smile 10 miles wide. We both say good morning as he entered the apartment. He asked me how it was going. I responded with its going well. I closed and locked the front door, and then I offered him a seat. I told him he could pick one of the two leather high-back bar chairs in front of the kitchen island counter. It divided the living room from the kitchen. I thought it was the perfect place for him to sit so we could talk while I finished cooking breakfast. I later thought he was sizing me up because, at times, I had to turn my back to him while facing the stove. When I wasn't facing the stove, I could stand facing him at the kitchen sink when washing my dishes or just talking back and forth.

It was 8:30 AM, and I was fully dressed. I wonder if he thought he might have found me in my nightclothes. He was wrong and probably shocked that I wasn't. I made it my business always to get showered and dressed when I got up out of bed. I would even make my bed too. We talked back and forth about the weather. I told him that being from New York City, the school or companies never closed down over one inch of snow as it did here in Virginia.

We laughed about it, and then we talked about some warmer weather destination spots that would make great vacation getaways. Samrick told me how he felt we sister girls knew how to go away on trips together and have fun. I agreed with him! He asked me had I been to any great vacation places. I told him no, not as of yet. However, a trip to an island destination was on my bucket list.

It was time to serve my kids breakfast. I offered him a plate of food, and he accepted. I then called the kids to come get their plates. As they entered the room from out of their kid's cove, they spoke to Samrick as I introduced them to him. The kids grab their plates and head right back to their room, and shut the door. My two girls share the second bedroom, so they were really close and got along really well. They were in that preteen stage of life, so they had a lot to talk about with each other.

Samrick asked, "Are your girls always that quiet?"

I said, "Yes, pretty much."

He said, "I could not even tell they were here in

the house."

*And be not conformed to this world: but be ye transformed by the renewing of your mind, that ye may prove what is that good, and acceptable, and perfect, will of God. – Romans 12:2, KJV*

# No Voice, What Choice

He was so polite. He finished his plate of food and thanked me. Samrick told me how good the breakfast tasted. I smiled and told him thanks. He handed me his plate from across the kitchen island. I stood facing him and the kitchen sink. We continued our conversation while I finished washing the last few dishes. I always washed my dishes as I went along so it would be less of a mess when I finished cooking. He must have taken notes because he asked was I always so neat with my housekeeping. I told him yes, my mother did not play that when I was coming up, my room had to be clean before I left for school and when I returned home chores had to be done before I could go outside to play. *(Oh, no, Cynthia didn't play)*

I was ready to go sit down and relax in the living room. Then it dawned on me that I needed to sweep the kitchen floor. I grabbed the broom from the laundry room and began to get up any food crumbs I may have dropped while preparing breakfast. Samrick was still sitting at the kitchen island and watching me sweep. I was almost finished when he asked me if he could use my restroom. I wanted to say no because it felt strange having a man in my house, let alone using my bathroom. No man had been in my home since my husband had left. It felt strange because the Holy Ghost was trying to warn me. I knew in my mind I felt some kind of way about having piss on my bathroom floor and the toilet seat being left up was another reason I wanted to say no!

I put the broom back in the laundry room and close the door. Finally, I say sure you can use the restroom. I pointed in the direction of the bathroom and told him it's to his right straight down the hall. Now, mind you, the hall was only 10 feet long. You couldn't get lost unless you wanted to end up in my bedroom, which was at the end of the hall off to the left, or in my daughters' room which was on the left too, directly across from the bathroom. You had to be high or drunk or up to no good to get lost.

I decided to move the gathering to the living room. I waited for Mr. Smooth to return from the bathroom. I notice a long lapse in time, about eight minutes. I say to myself, *hold up an elephant doesn't take this long to drop a load.* I jump up off the couch and quickly walk to the bathroom. I was shocked. My heart skipped a beat. The door of the bathroom was wide open. No Samrick. No piss on the floor. No toilet seat up. No water splashes on the sink. No rumpled floor mats. Everything was just how I had left it this morning after my shower. The little night light was still on too.

*Brethren, if a man be overtaken in a fault, ye which are spiritual, restore such a one in the spirit of meekness; considering thyself, lest thou also be tempted. – Galatians 6:1*

# You Don't Know Me

Where was this joker? The apartment was only so big. My heart started pumping fast with fear. I prayed, *no, God, don't tell me this man is in my girls' room messing with them.* Oh my God!!

Just as I was about to burst into my girls' bedroom, I noticed my bedroom door was partially closed. I know goodness well I had left my bedroom door all the way open. The only time my bedroom door was closed was when my husband and I made love, or we were getting dressed. Outside of that, our bedroom door was always open. I slowly push the door open. Then I notice a black something on the floor. I say, *oh no, Lord, don't tell me this creep has passed out on my bedroom floor.* First of all, what in the world is he doing in my bedroom? As I examine the pile on the floor from the bedroom door entrance, I realize it wasn't a body, but a man's pants, belt, underwear, socks, and shoes!

What kind of nut have I allowed in my home? Tell me, what devil is bold enough to come into a strange woman's home with her kids present and front like he has to use the restroom and then go to her bedroom and get butterball naked? The nerve of this negro.

30

I walked into the bedroom to confront him. That's when he grabbed me from behind, putting his hand over my mouth. He put me in a bear hug and held my arms and body so I could not run. He took one foot and pushed the door shut while at the same time moving my body with the weight of his 200 plus frame towards my bed. I push back, trying to use my weight to halt his maneuver – his maneuver to tackle me onto the bed. My efforts failed. He picked me up like I was a paper doll, threw me down onto the bed, took his solid-build frame, and lay all of his weight on top of me. I was struggling, twisting and turning while at the same time struggling to breathe. It felt like my lungs weren't able to expand fully because of the heaviness of his body on top of mine. He had me in some kind of wrestler hold. Still holding his hand over my mouth and breathing hard in my ear, he squeezed my two wrists together with his other hand and pinned them really hard onto the pillow that lay lopsided beneath my head and his face. He took his strong muscular legs and tried to pry open my legs, but I wouldn't let him.

He got mad and started throwing me around like I was a football, and he was an NFL linebacker. Then he got still and whispered in my ear, "Why are you crying?" still holding his hand over my mouth. The pillow was wet with my tears so was the side of his neck and cheek. I ask myself, do I scream. I can't. Do I run? I can't and leave my kids. I cry, more so embarrassed that I opened my door to a stranger, and he is now violating me. I am trying to keep my girls safe. I do not know if he will kill me or my girls, so there will not be any witnesses, so I don't scream out.

Who is this beast with the fresh fade haircut, the manicured nails, sunny bright smile, pleasant disposition? Who is this person who seemed warm and kind but is really cold-hearted and hateful? He seemed so intelligent but is really dumb. Who is this person that seemed so caring but is really mean and cruel?

He went limp after he ejaculated inside of me. Weeping, I pushed him off me. I lay in disbelief, thinking, what if this man has AIDS? Did he come here to rape and infect me on purpose? He got up as cold as a six-pack of Heineken beer, showing no emotion, no remorse, no pity, no shame – nothing!

I asked him, "Why did you do this?"

He spoke only three words after putting his clothes back on, "I don't know."

Then he left.

*Know ye not, that to whom ye yield yourselves servants to obey, his servants ye are to whom ye obey; whether of sin unto death, or of obedience unto righteousness? – Romans 6:16, KJV*

# When You Practice Sin

It becomes easy to violate God's laws and violate others too when you practice sin.

Things were starting to look up for the children and me. I had been blessed with a job at a major credit card company as a customer service representative. I saw my rape counselor on a regular for therapy. It had been three months since the rape happened. I never reported it to the police because I was fearful that I would be put on trial and asked why I let a stranger in my home.

My husband was still AWOL, and he still did not know what had happened to me. Besides, my husband was upset with me because I filed for child support and spousal support. It only made sense, being that I had the kids and all the responsibility that came with keeping a roof over our head, feeding, clothing, co-pay for doctors, dentists, orthodontics, and not to mention shoes and clothes for growing teens. Our youngest ran track, so that was an expense all by itself. Three females having monthly cycles, which was another bill too for personal items.

I was wondering who and what made my husband call me from his job. I was not allowed to take personal calls while on the call center floor. I guess employees could steal clients' personal banking information, so cell phones were off and limited. I kept my phone on vibrate because I had girls. I needed them to be able to text me if necessary. I had just finished a call with a customer when I noticed the prefix 380, which was the same prefix number for the shipyard where my husband had worked for the last 10 years. I quickly hit the phone buttons to log myself out for a five-minute bathroom break. I rushed to the back stairwell and swiftly answered the phone to take my husband's phone call.

"Hello, how are you?"

I paused. To my disgust, it was Samrick calling me from the shipyard. I guess it was his office phone.

"What is your freaking problem calling me? You know I should report your black behind to the cops."

"Wait, wait!" he says.

"Heck no! Wait for what?!?! Why in the world did you do that to me?"

"Do what?"

"Rape me!! Samrick Clark, you are a sick person with a sick mind," I yelled in the phone.

"I have needs."

"What? You have needs?!?!" I screamed. "So does a dog, but what does that have to do with me?"

"I have something to tell you."

I yelled, "What? You got AIDS?"

"No," he mumbled, "No."

"What? Are you married?"

"No," he stated.

"What do you have to tell me?"

Stuttering, he says, " I am a Pastor."

"WHAT?!?!"

"I am a Pastor, and yes, I am married too."

I flipped out and said, "Oh no. Oh no. Oh, my God. How could you?!?!"

I shook my head in total disbelief. I collapsed on the cement staircase in tears. I thought that any moment the back staircase doorway would open with my supervisor telling me I was in trouble for taking an extended backroom break, or worst I was being written up for making a ruckus in the stairwell while agents were on the phone talking to customers.

No one came out to get me, and I was relieved because my whole face was a mess with streaks of tears and make-up that I had just started wearing. After all, I needed to make myself feel better about the whole ordeal of being raped and my husband being AWOL. Plus, my counselor said it was okay for me to be okay with being nice to myself, so I started wearing a little eye shadow and mascara. I could not believe my ears and what he was telling me.

He replied, "You caught my attention the first time I saw you because you had on a dress, heels, and stockings, and none of your body parts were exposed. You were covered up, and that made me curious to see and feel what it would be like to have you."

"Sir, you don't even know me. I could have AIDS!!"

"I doubt that. Besides, I know you have been married a while, which means you have probably only been with your husband. So I felt it was safe to have you."

I was shocked. He was sizing me up! He said the morning he came to my house, he made several observations about my surroundings. He told me that the first thing he noticed was I was fully dressed, with no hair scarf, no rollers, no pajama pants, fully clothed, including undergarments. As far as he could tell, I guess because my breasts weren't sagging and my behind was not shaking like jello all over the place, he could tell I had on undergarments. He mentioned that my house and living room were immaculate. No dust anywhere, the pillows on the sofa and loveseat were fluffed and neatly arranged, and the coffee table and end table had glass mirror tops, and he could see his reflection. He pointed out that he noticed I did not have any dirty dishes in the sink and washed all my dishes as I prepared breakfast. He told me he could not tell I had kids either because the apartment looked as if I lived there alone. I told him just because it looked like I had it all together, maybe I have OCD, but that's no reason to rape someone. He did not know that between my late Bishop, the late first lady, and my mother, I was trained on being a lady, a good housekeeper, and a cook.

I said to him, "Don't you ever call me again, or else I will be sure to send the police straight to your job and arrest you for rape."

I hung up the phone, wiped my face, got myself together, and headed back to work.

A few years later, I saw him at the Minister's Conference. He spoke to me with the nod of his head. I spoke to him with the wave of my hand like *Sir, bye*.

A week later, my cell phone rang. The caller ID said – Private!!

*I, therefore, the prisoner of the Lord, beseech you that ye walk worthy of the vocation wherewith ye are called.*
*– Ephesians 4:1, KJV*

# Date Rape

Date rape definition: Rape committed by a person who has been socializing or on a date with the victim.

**Source:** www.yourdictionary.com

"Out of every 1,000 sexual assaults, 310 are reported to the police."

**Source:** www.rainn.org/statistics

"Every 73 seconds, an American is sexually assaulted, and every nine minutes that victim is a child."

**Source:** www.rainn.org/statistics

**National Sexual Assault Hotline: 800-656-HOPE(4673)**

CPSIA information can be obtained
at www.ICGtesting.com
Printed in the USA
JSHW020753010621
15409JS00001B/4